Rock Shock

Tony Bradman • Jon Stuart

Contents

OXFORD
UNIVERSITY PRESS

 This page is for an adult to read to you.

Macro Marvel
(billionaire inventor)

Welcome to Micro World!

Macro Marvel invented Micro World – a micro-sized theme park where you have to shrink to get in.

A computer called ***CODE*** controls Micro World and all the robots inside – MITEs and BITEs.

A MITE

A BITE

Disaster strikes!

CODE goes wrong on opening day.
CODE wants to shrink the world.

Macro Marvel is trapped inside the park …

 This page is for an adult to read to you.

Enter Team X!

Four micro agents – ***Max, Cat, Ant*** and ***Tiger*** – are sent to rescue Macro Marvel and defeat CODE.

Mini Marvel joins Team X.

Mini Marvel
(Macro's daughter)

In the last book ...

- Ant and Tiger woke the BITE when they entered the pyramid using the Driller.
- They shrank and climbed up the BITE to try to get the CODE key.

CODE key
(11 collected)

You are in the Pyramid Peril zone.

 This page is for an adult to read with you.

Before you read

Sound checker

The sound to remember when you are reading this book.

si

Word alert

Blend the sounds. Remember the sound you have practised.

deci**s**ion vi**s**ion
trea**s**ures

Into the zone

- What do you already know about the BITE?
- Can you remember how Max, Cat, Mini and Rex got trapped?

The Mummy-BITE

Max, Cat, Mini and Rex were trapped inside the pyramid. Mini had a strange feeling that the BITE was somewhere inside the pyramid, too. She looked up the BITE on her Gizmo.

Mummy-BITE

Things to look out for ...

The BITE sets traps to surprise intruders.

lurks deep inside the pyramid

sand trap

beetle trap

Attack!

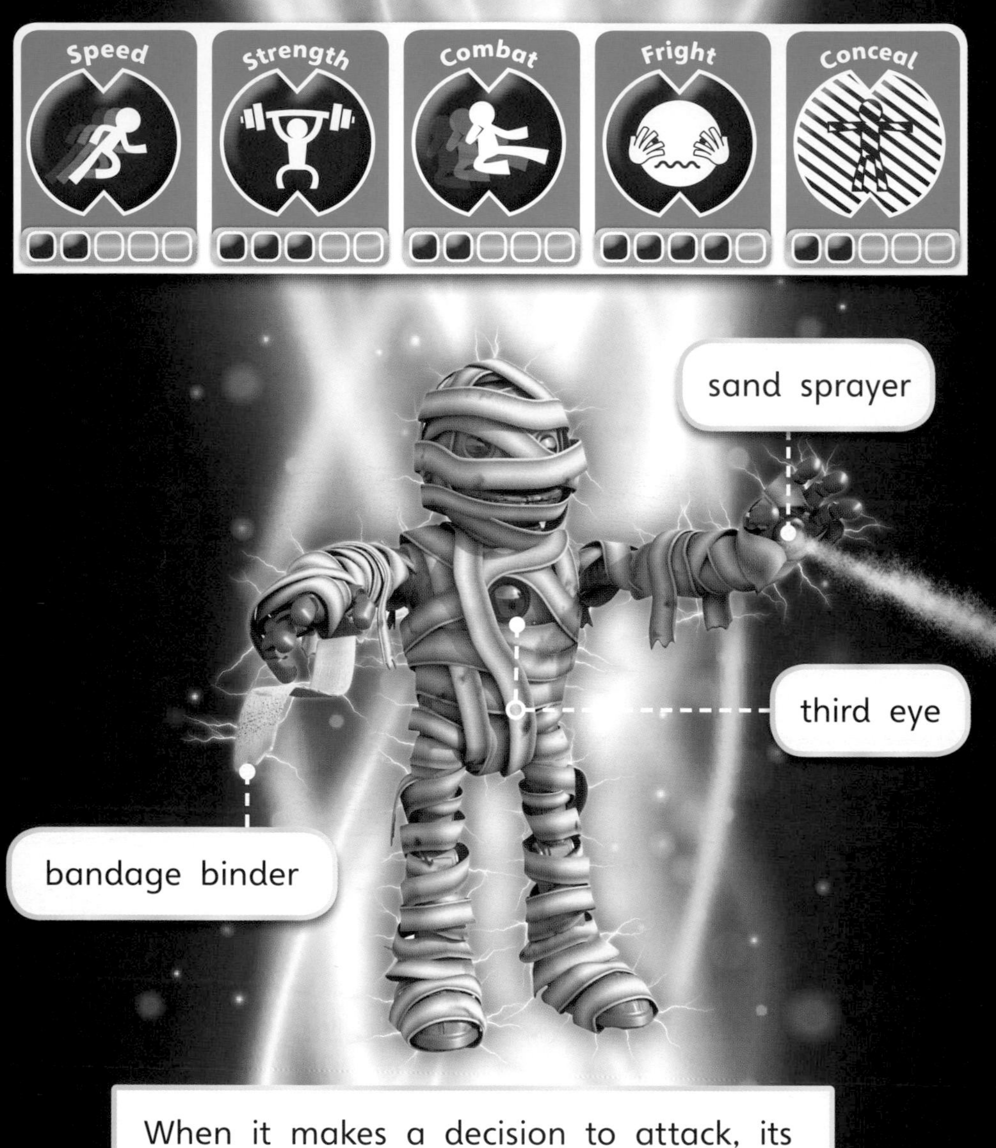

When it makes a decision to attack, its bandages loosen to reveal a third eye.

The Mummy-BITE has extra powerful vision. Holding the eye in its hand, the BITE can see round corners and into dark shadows.

"I'm terrified of meeting this BITE," said Mini, putting away her Gizmo.

Just then a distant cry echoed through the pyramid.

"Do you think that was the BITE?" asked Cat.

"It sounded awful," whispered Mini.

"There's only one way to find out," said Max. "Come on. We'll have to face this BITE sometime!"

“Look at all these treasures and pictures,” said Mini.
“We don’t have time to stop and look around,” said Max. “We have to head deep inside the pyramid.”
“Yes, that’s where the BITE will be,” Cat replied.

 This page is for an adult to read with you.

Now you have read ...

The Mummy-BITE

Take a closer look

What three things can the Mummy-BITE do when it attacks?

Thinking time

Fill in the gaps using the parts of the sentence below.

it has left the pyramid	Max, Cat and Mini have to leave the pyramid to find the BITE	the BITE lurks deep inside the pyramid

The Gizmo says ______________ but ______________,
so ______________.

This BITE sounds really scary!

 This page is for an adult to read with you.

Before you read

Word alert

- Read the words. Remember the sound you practised in 'The Mummy-BITE'.

explosion confusion

measure

- Look out for other words that include this sound when you are reading.

What does it mean?

confusion – feeling muddled and unsure

hurtling – moving very fast

Into the zone

- What have Max, Cat and Mini decided to do?
- Do you know what ancient Egyptian writing was like?

Don't Look Back!

Chapter 1 – A Rumble in the Dark

Max, Cat, Mini and Rex were searching for the BITE inside the pyramid. Mini wasn't looking forward to finding this key.

Suddenly, a loud explosion boomed through the pyramid. It was followed by a deep, rumbling sound.

“What was that?” asked Cat in confusion.

Max went to investigate. He came racing back at once.
“Run!” Max shouted. “It’s another trap!”

A huge ball of rock was hurtling down the passage towards them.

"How big is this thing?" yelled Cat, panting.

"I don't know!" said Max. "I'm not going to stop to measure it! Just keep running!"

"STOP!" yelled Cat, suddenly.
They skidded to a halt at the edge of a deep, dark pit. Behind them, the giant ball of rock was gaining speed. They looked towards the other side of the pit – it was a long way across!

Chapter 2 – Hold Tight!

Max made a quick decision. He fired the wire from his watch.

"Quick, grab the wire!" yelled Max. Cat and Mini hung on as Max swung across the pit. The rock just missed them and plunged into the pit below.

"We're safe!" said Mini. "That was quick thinking, Max."
Then they heard another explosion.
"Oh, no!" said Mini, "That sounds like more traps!"
"Quick!" said Cat. "Let's hide in there."

"We can't hide here forever," said Max. "We've got to find a way out."

"How?" asked Cat. "The door is closed. Even if we could make it back to the entrance, I bet that's shut, too."

"Wait a minute," said Mini. "I think there might be another way out."

Mini pointed to some Egyptian pictures on the wall. There was a picture of a small doorway. Next to it were pictures of MITEs going down a passage leading to the desert outside.

"I'm sure the pictures are telling us there's a secret passage," said Mini.

Chapter 3 – Another Way Out

They began to search for a doorway out of the chamber. Rex soon found it near a gold treasure chest.

Max, Cat, Mini and Rex made their way along a dark tunnel.

They saw a door up ahead.
“We’ve made it!” cheered Cat as they crawled out of the pyramid.

"Oh, no! Look!" cried Mini. "It's the BITE!"
"Remember, this BITE has powerful vision,"
said Cat. "We need to hide."
They shrank quickly and hid behind
some rocks.

The ground shook as the BITE stomped past.

"I hope that powerful third eye doesn't see us," Max whispered.

"We should be safe here," said Mini. "What about Ant and Tiger? Where are they?"

Cat followed the tracker on her watch.
"I think Ant and Tiger are somewhere on the BITE!" she said.
"Oh no!" cried Mini. "We have to help them!"

 This page is for an adult to read with you.

Now you have read ...

Don't Look Back!

Take a closer look

What was the trap in this story?

What or who do you think set it off?

Thinking time

Choose a character and describe what they might say, think and feel as they swing across the pit.

We must help Ant and Tiger!